NEXT STATION

STARTER S

WORKBOOK

Amanda Cant / Mary Charrington

CONTENTS

Unit	VOCABULARY	GRAMMAR	FEATURES
1 PAGES 3-10	hello, goodbye, bye, yes, no one, two, three, four, five, six, seven, eight, nine, ten	I'm (Roberto). I'm (six).	The World **World Music Song:** Welcome to Next Station
2 PAGES 11-18	pencil, eraser, pen, pencil case, ruler backpack, chair, glue stick, crayon, book	It's a (pencil). It's an (eraser). one (book) two (books)	**Country:** South Korea **World Music Song:** Welcome to Korea
3 PAGES 19-26	red, blue, yellow, pink, green gray, black, white, brown, orange	It's (red). My (pencil) is (pink).	**Country:** Brazil **World Music Song:** Welcome to Brazil
4 PAGES 27-34	ball, puppet, guitar, scooter, teddy bear doll, yo-yo, bike, kite, video game	I have a (puppet). I have a (red) (kite).	**Country:** Mexico **World Music Song:** Welcome to Mexico
5 PAGES 35-42	head, arms, hands, legs, feet eyes, ears, nose, mouth, hair	This is my (head). These are my (arms). I have (a nose). I have (two eyes).	**Country:** Ireland **World Music Song:** Welcome to Ireland
6 PAGES 43-50	mom, dad, grandma, grandpa, sister, brother big, small, old, young	This is my (mom). My (grandma) is (old).	**Country:** Vietnam **World Music Song:** Welcome to Vietnam
7 PAGES 51-58	lion, giraffe, elephant, monkey, zebra goat, donkey, hen, cow, dog	It's (brown) and (yellow). They're (hens).	**Country:** Botswana **World Music Song:** Welcome to Botswana
8 PAGES 59-66	hat, shirt, skirt, sweater, pants T-shirt, dress, socks, shoes, shorts	It's my (hat). They're my (pants). It's your (hat). They're your (shoes).	**Country:** Peru **World Music Song:** Welcome to Peru
9 PAGES 67-74	rice, orange, banana, fish, salad pizza, pasta, fries, juice, water	I like (salad). I don't like (fish). Do you like (pasta)? Yes, I do. / No, I don't.	**Country:** Italy **World Music Song:** Welcome to Italy
10 PAGES 75-82	bedroom, living room, bathroom, kitchen, yard table, TV, closet, bed, sofa	I'm in the (bedroom). There's a (bed) in the (bedroom).	**Country:** USA **World Music Song:** Welcome to the USA

PAGES 83-94 CRAFT ACTIVITIES

PAGE 95 PROGRESS RECORD

TRACK 2

1 Listen and point. 

VOCABULARY

1 Complete and say.

Lesson 2

1 Draw and say.

GRAMMAR

I'm (Roberto).

· PRACTICE ·

1 Draw a ◯ around *Yes* and a ☐ around *No*.

VOCABULARY

TRACK 9

1 Listen and point. 

1 2 3 4

5 6 7

8 9 10

Lesson 5

GRAMMAR

I'm (six).

1 Match and say.

· PRACTICE ·

1 Draw and say.

STORY TIME

1 Make and say.

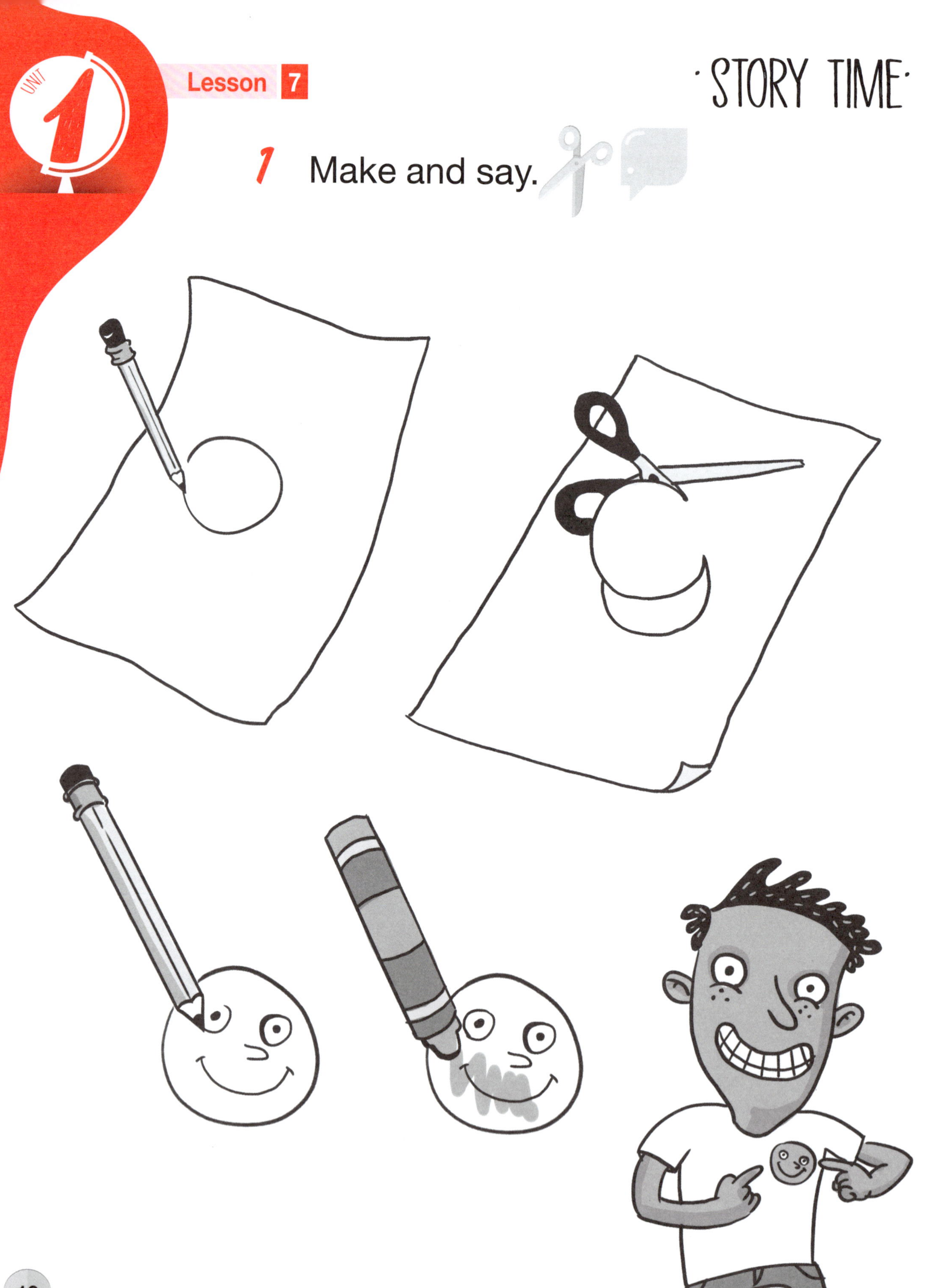

TRACK 12

1 Listen and point.

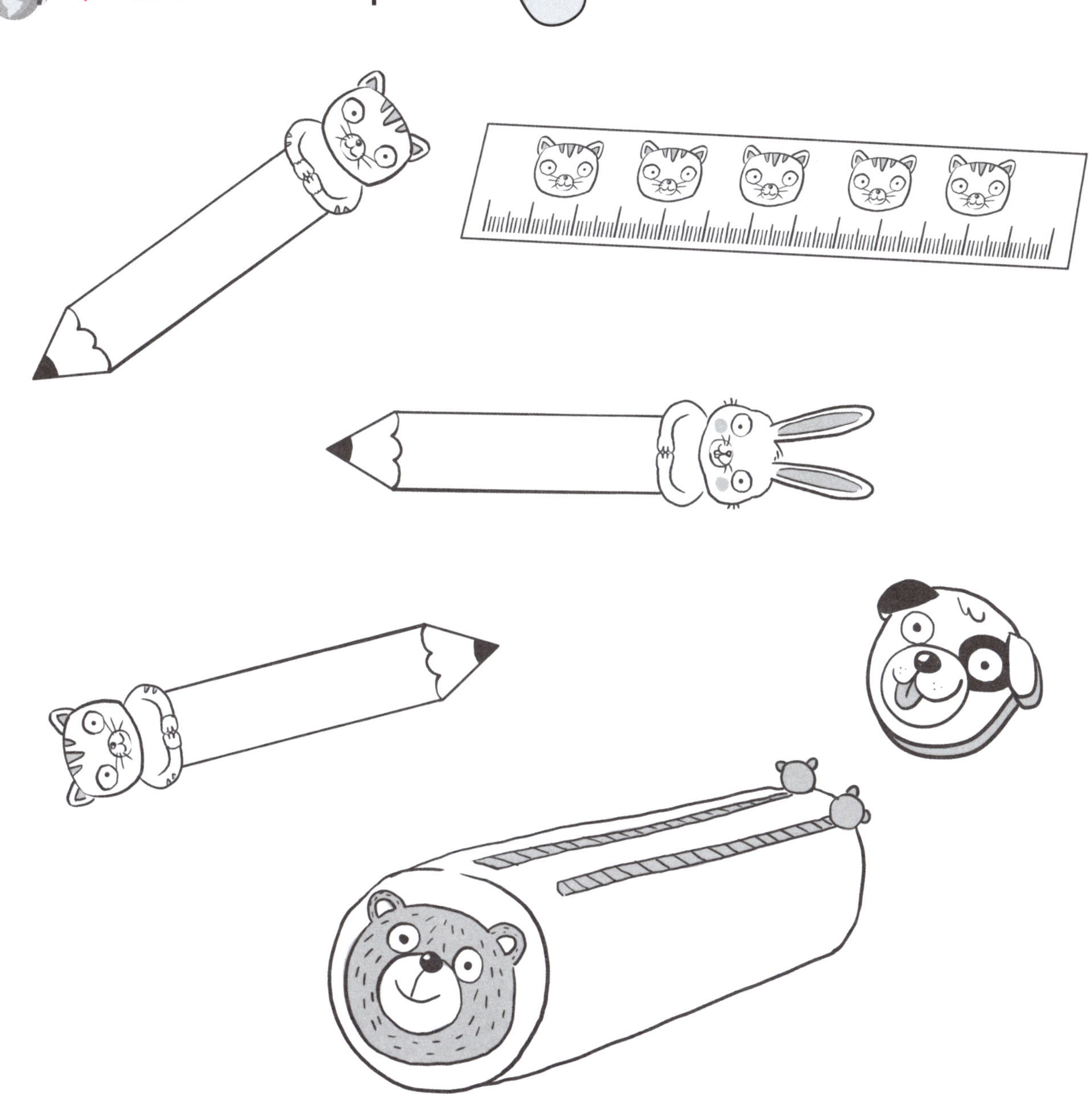

1 Complete and color.

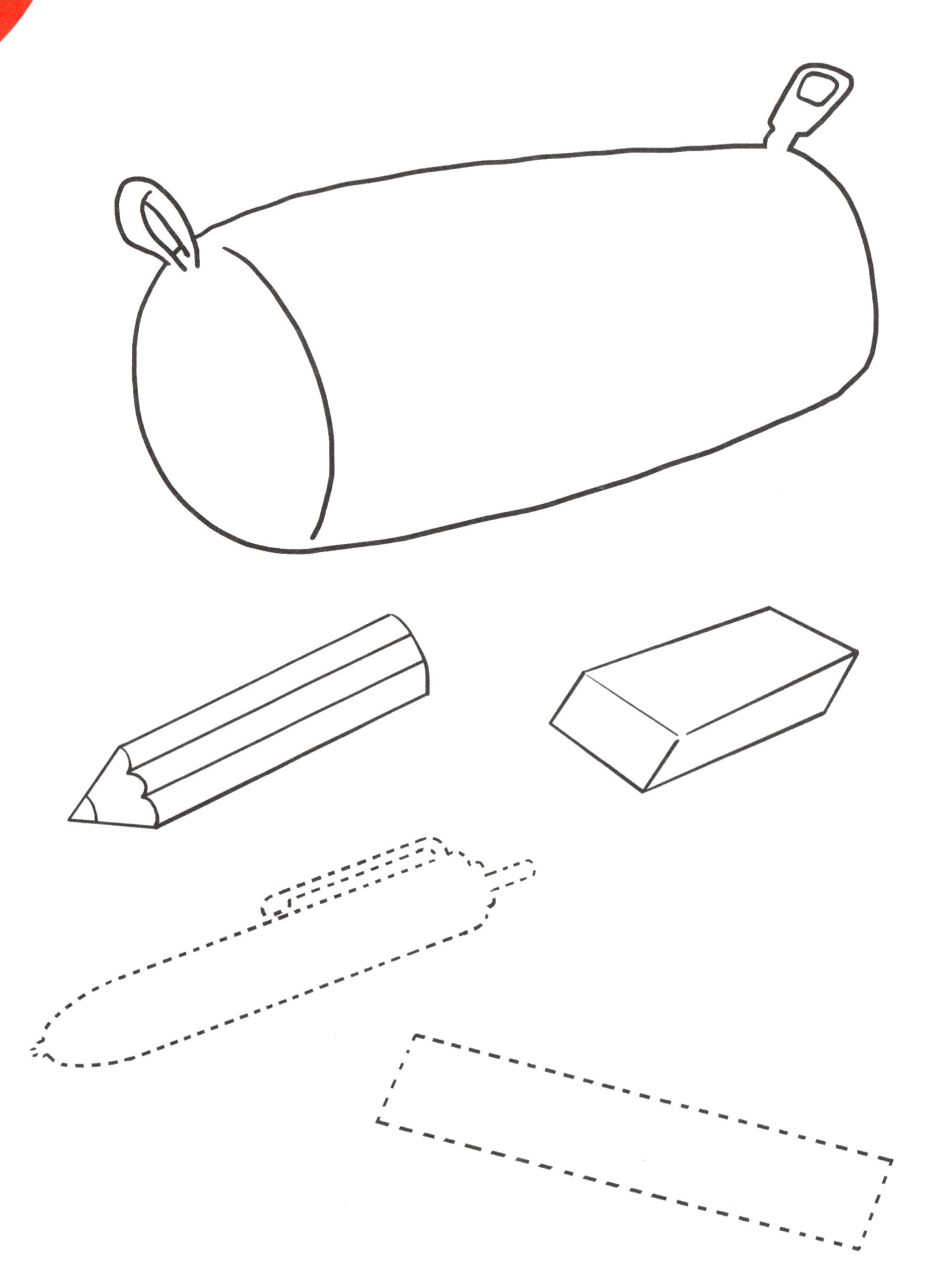

Lesson 2

1 Follow and say.

> **· GRAMMAR ·**
>
> It's a (pencil).
> It's an (eraser).

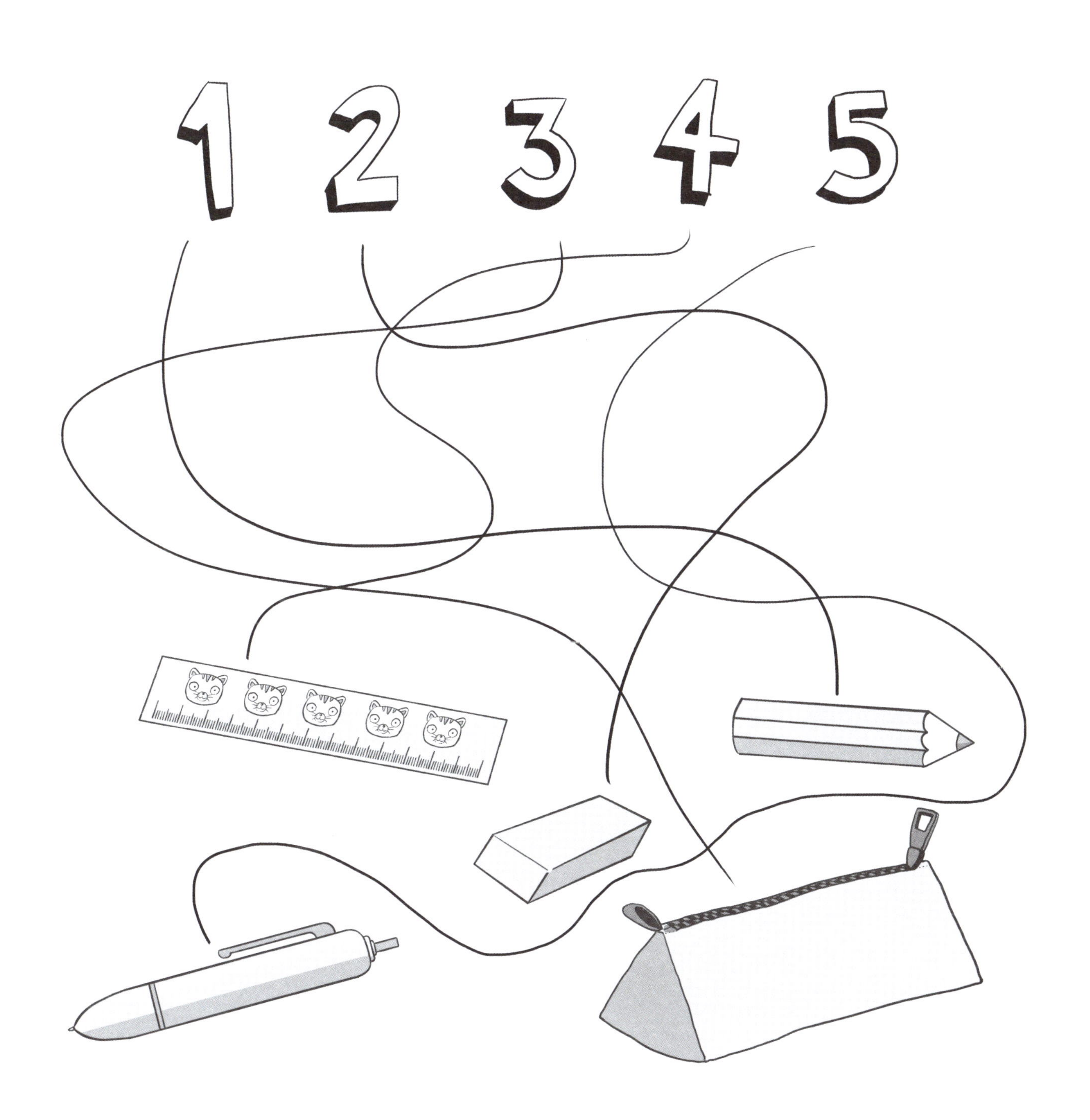

· PRACTICE ·

1 Complete and say.

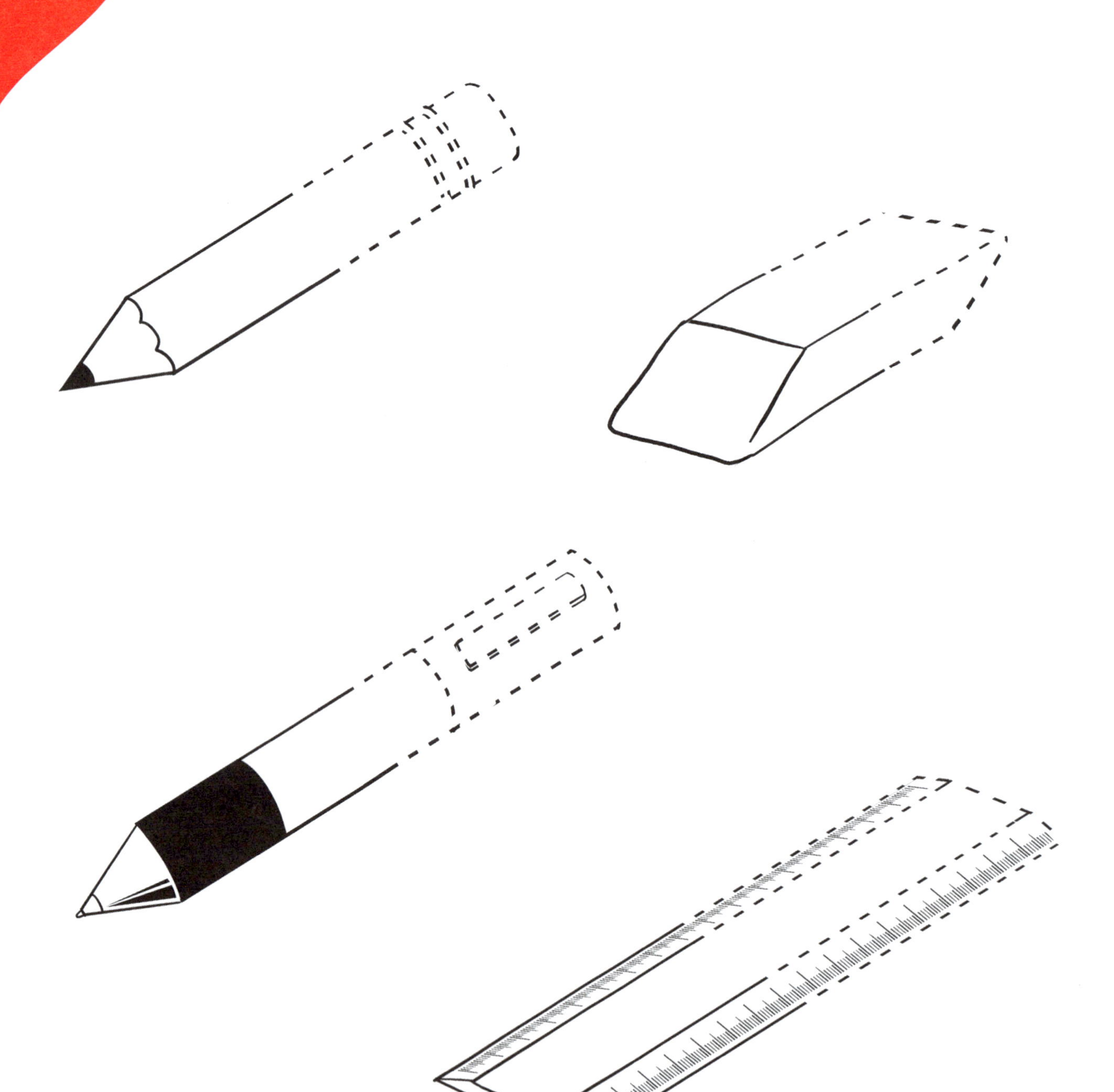

TRACK 17

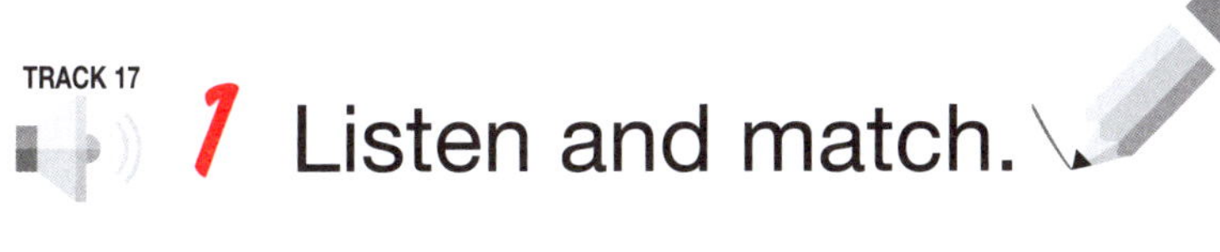
1 Listen and match.

Lesson 5

GRAMMAR

one (book)
two (books)

1 Draw a ◯ and count.

     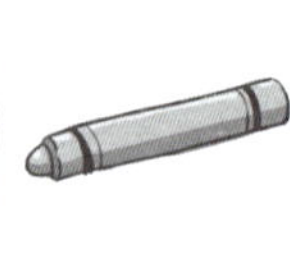  

   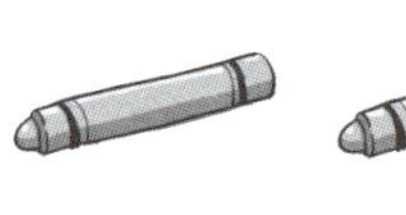 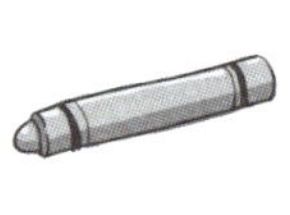 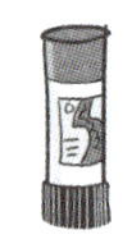 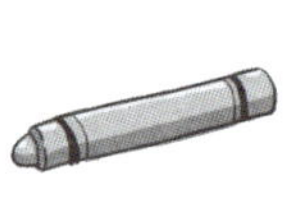 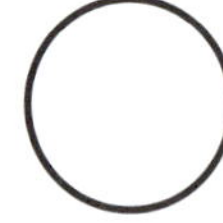

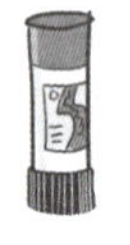  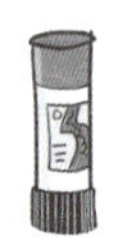 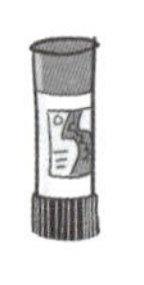  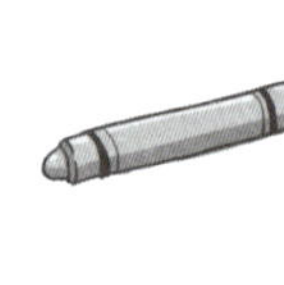  

  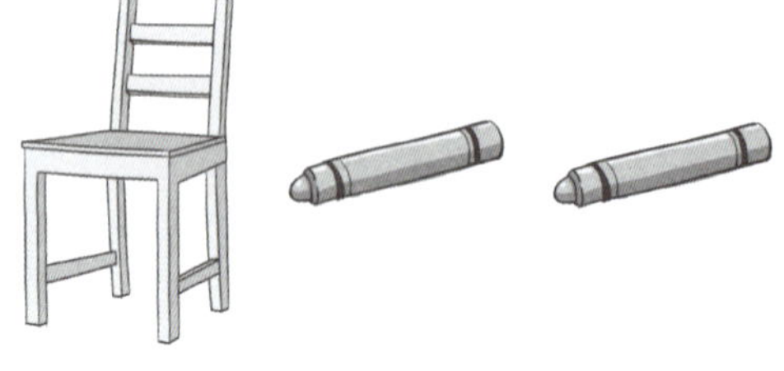 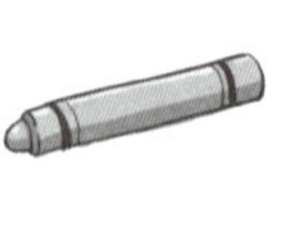 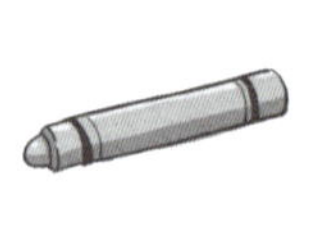 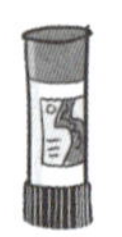 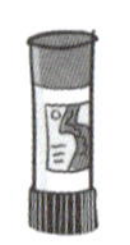 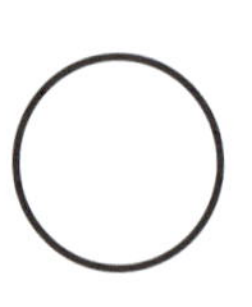

       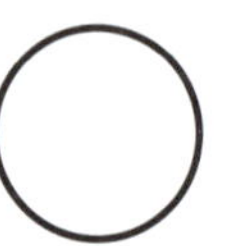

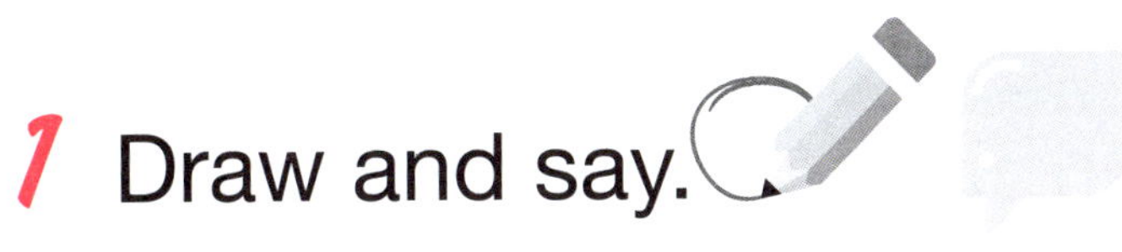

1 Draw and say.

4

2

5

1 Number.

TRACK 22

1 Listen and color.

VOCABULARY

1 Complete and say.

Lesson 2

1 Color and say.

· GRAMMAR ·

It's (red).

1 Make a color key. Color and say.

TRACK 29

1 Listen and color.

1

2

3

4

Lesson 5

GRAMMAR

My (pencil) is (pink).

1 Color and say.

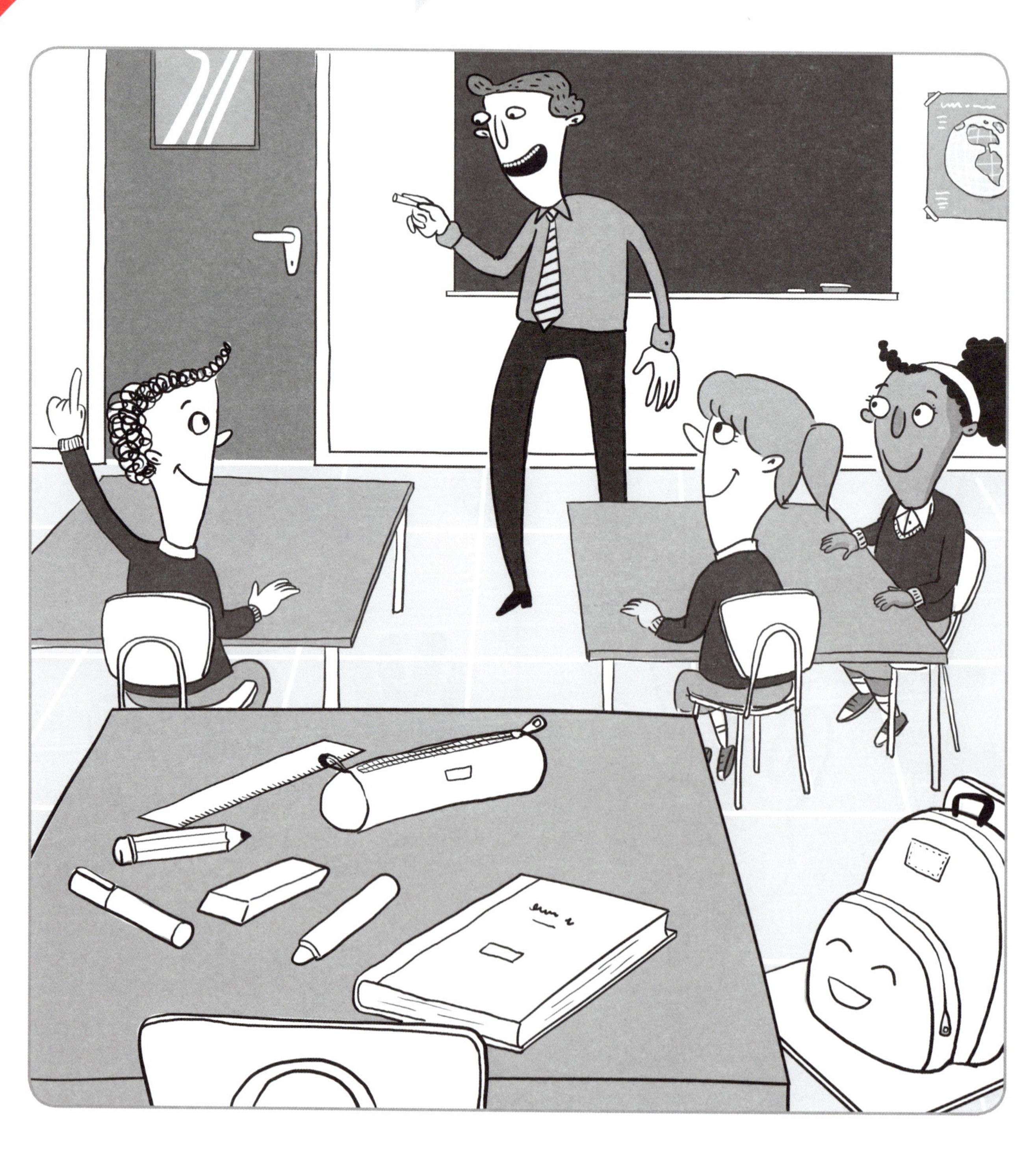

1 Color and match.

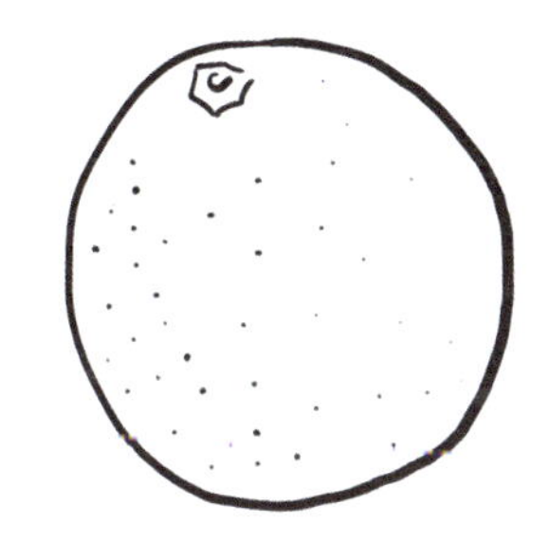

· STORY TIME ·

1 Draw and say. 

10 2 9 3 1

8 4

7 5

6

TRACK 32

1 Listen and point.

1 Number and color.

Lesson 2

1 Draw and say.

GRAMMAR

I have a (puppet).

PRACTICE

1 Color and say.

TRACK 39

1 Listen and point.

Lesson 5

1 Circle.

GRAMMAR

I have a (red) (kite).

1 Match and color.

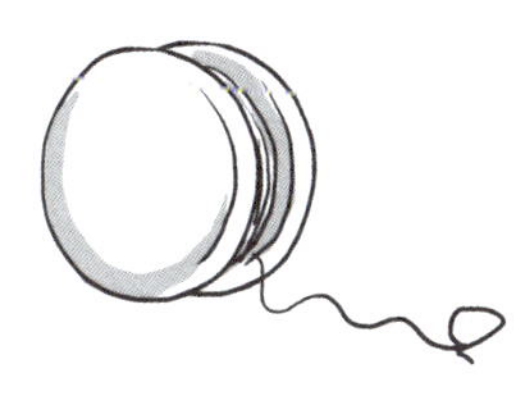

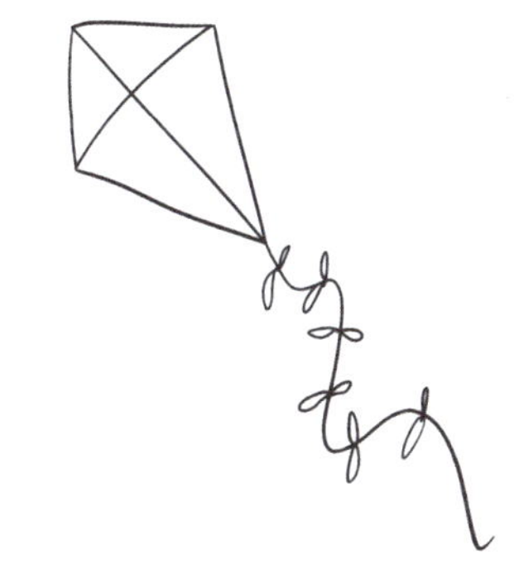

Lesson 7

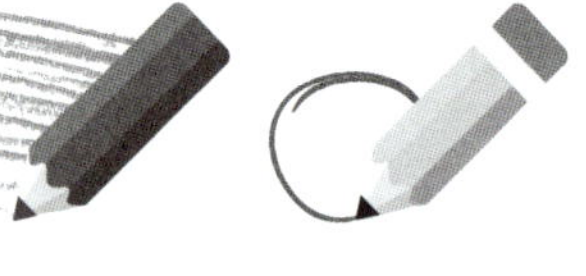

1 Color and complete.

TRACK 46

1 Listen and point.

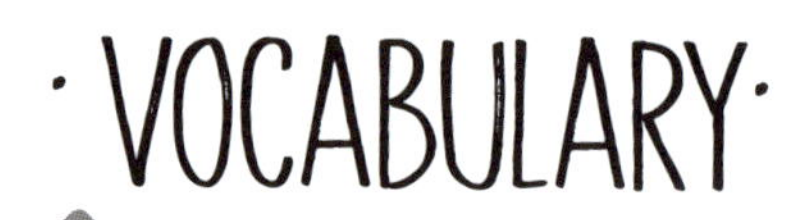

1 Complete and say.

Lesson 2

GRAMMAR

This is my (head).
These are my (arms).

1 Follow and say.

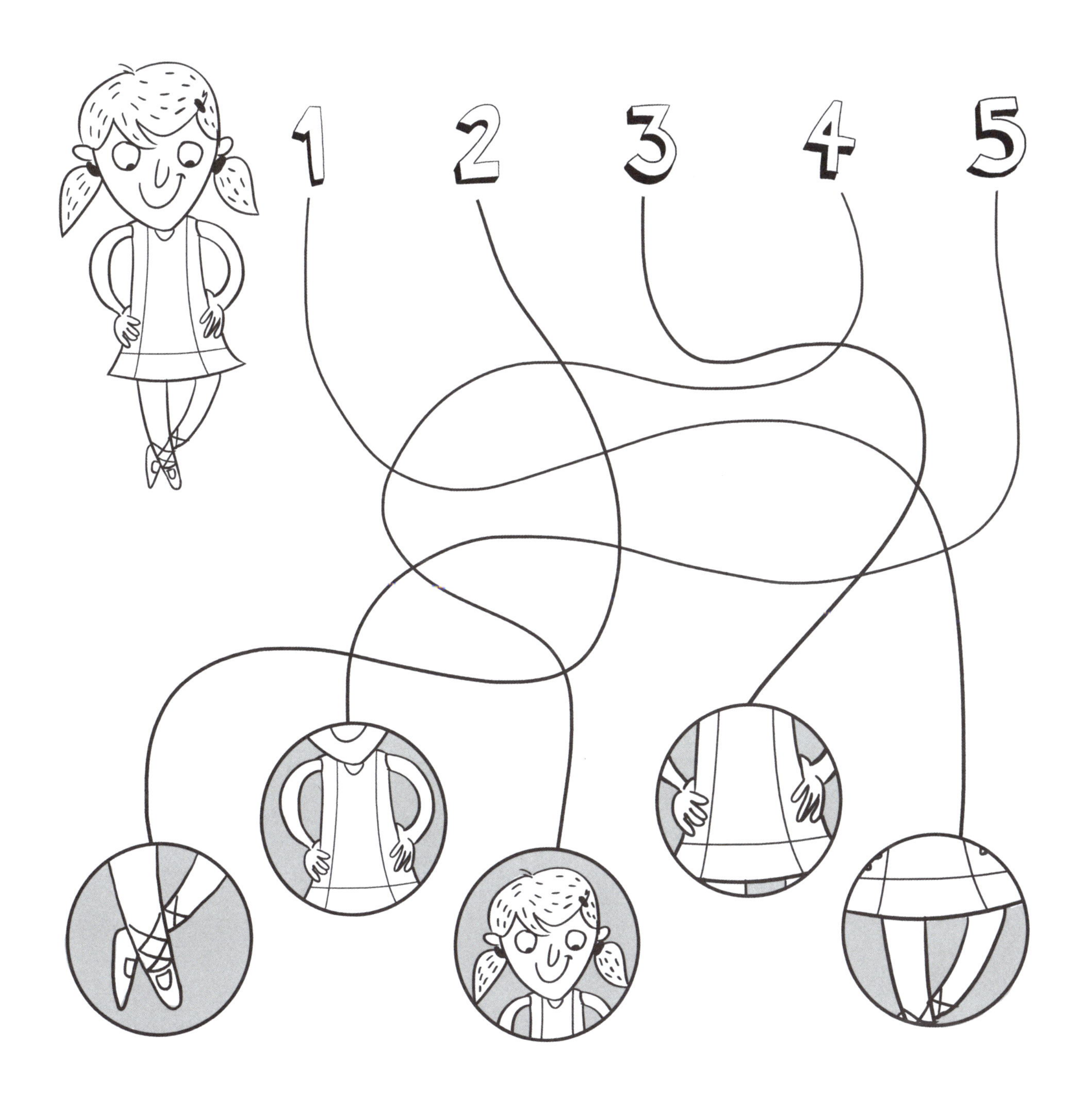

PRACTICE

1 Match and say.

VOCABULARY

TRACK 53

1 Listen and number.

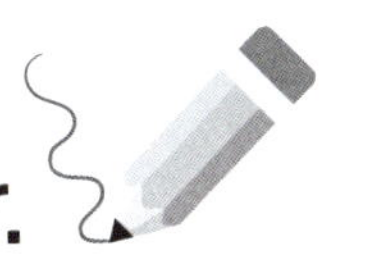

Lesson 5

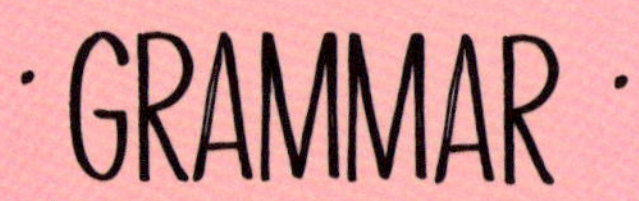

GRAMMAR

I have (a nose).
I have (two eyes).

1 Match.

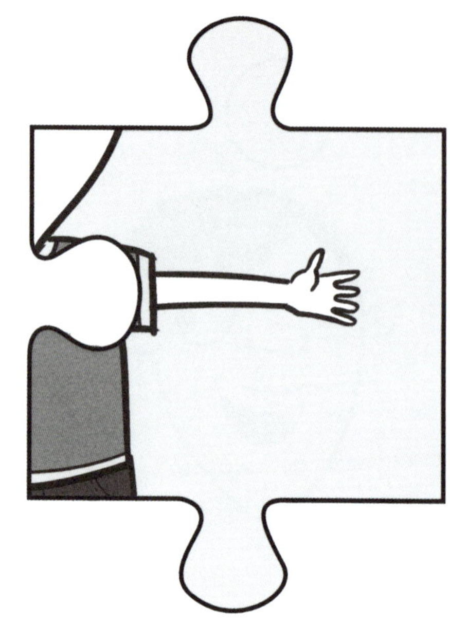

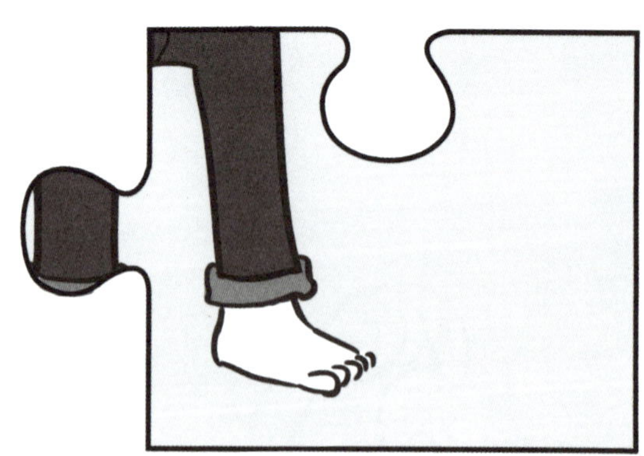

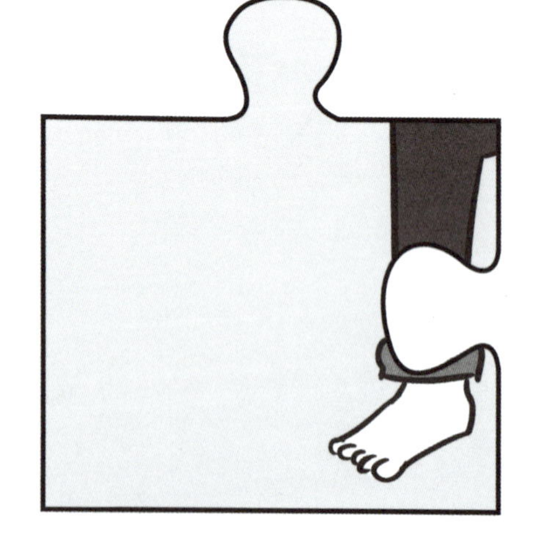

1 Draw and color.

Lesson 7

1 Draw.

TRACK 58

1 Listen and draw.

VOCABULARY

1 Point and say.

2 Draw.

Lesson 2

GRAMMAR

This is my (mom).

1 Find and number.

Then say.

· PRACTICE ·

1 Match and say.

TRACK 63

1 Listen and color.

GRAMMAR

My (grandma) is (old).

1 Circle and say.

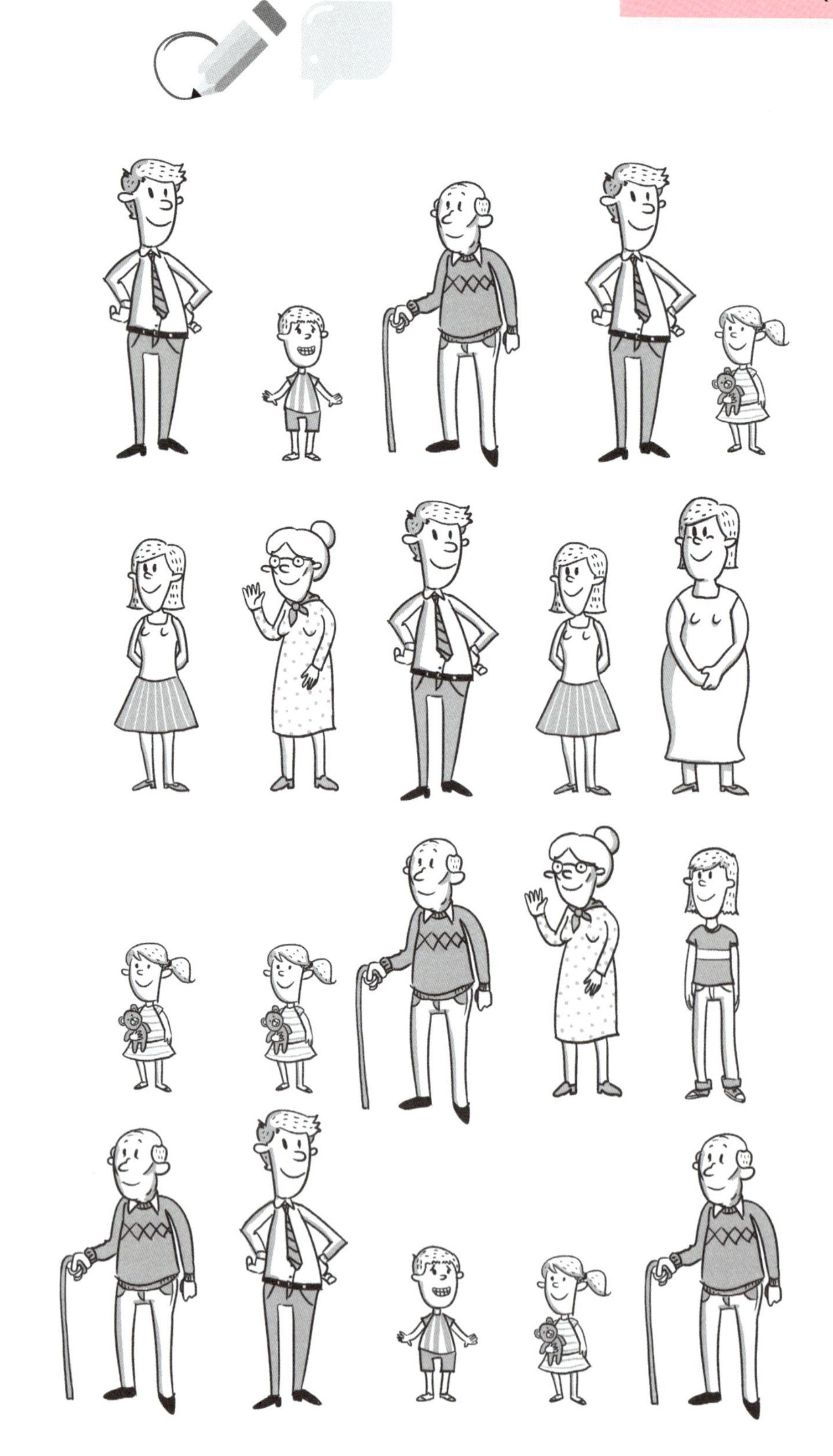

1 Draw and say.

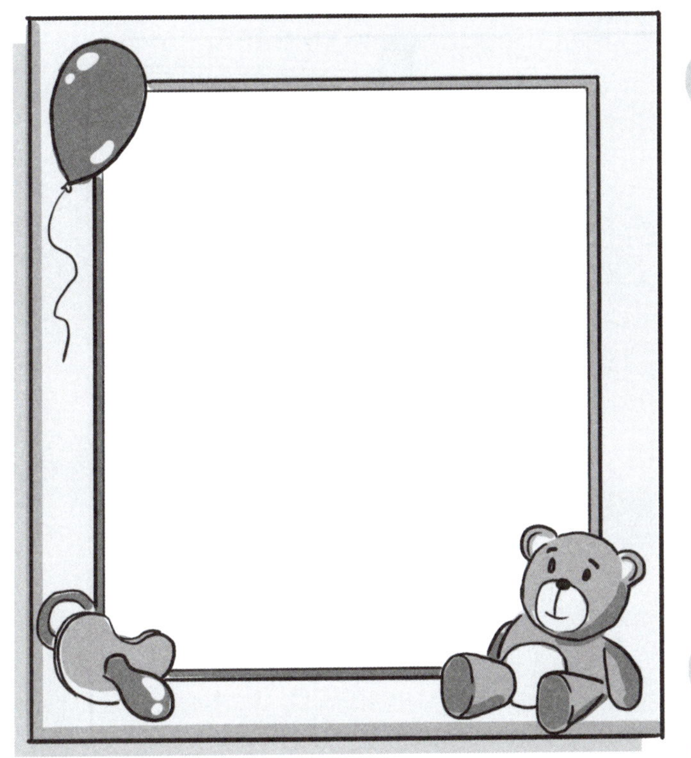

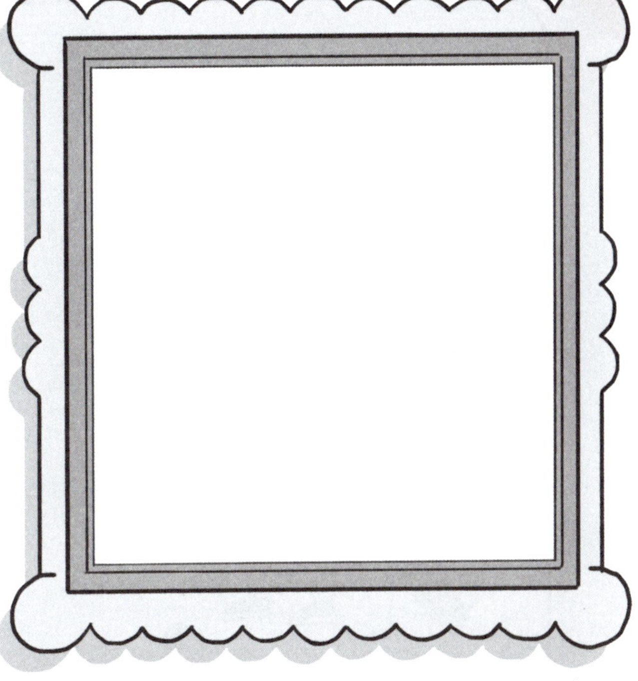

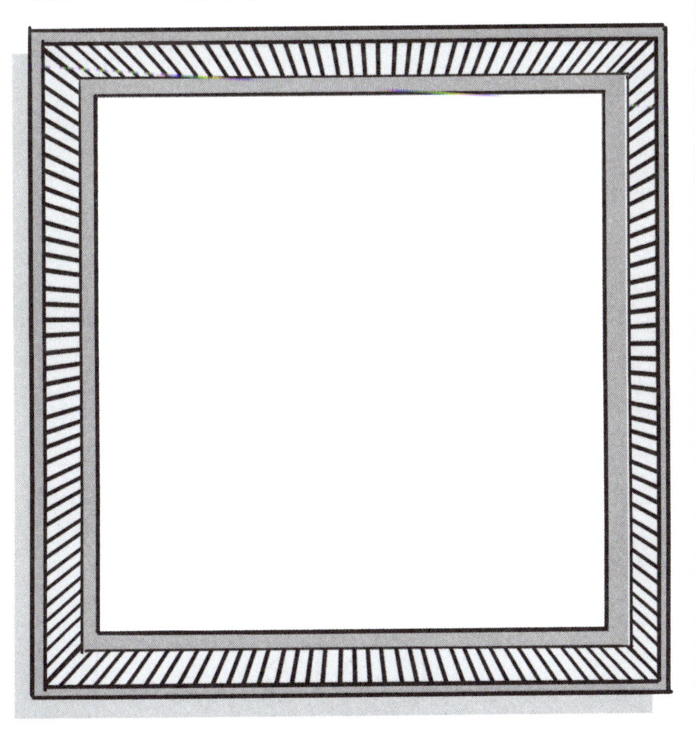

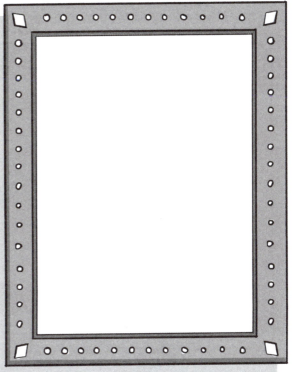

STORY TIME

TRACK 70

1 Listen and complete.

1 Draw and say. 

Lesson 2

1 Color and say.

GRAMMAR

It's (brown) and (yellow).

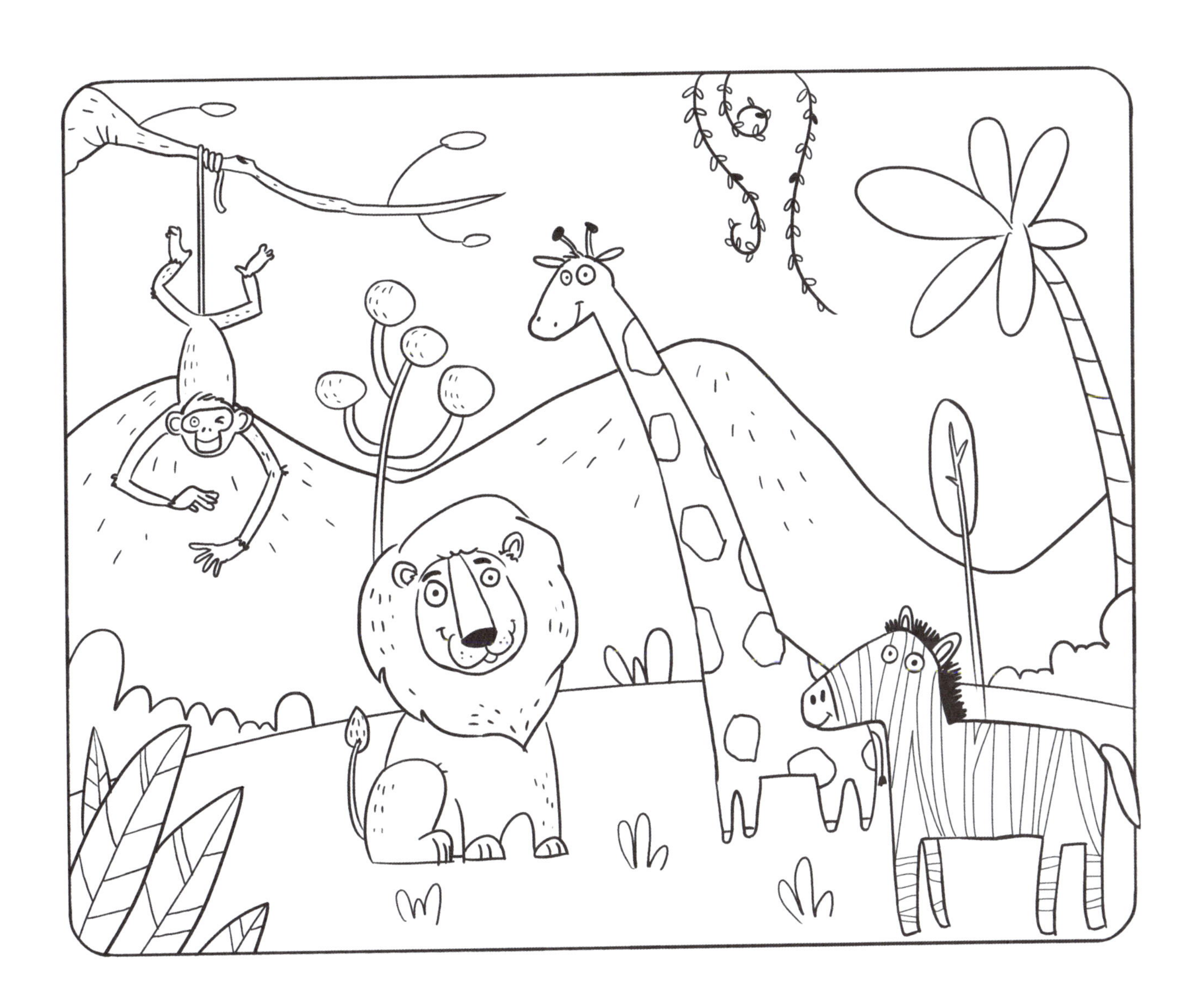

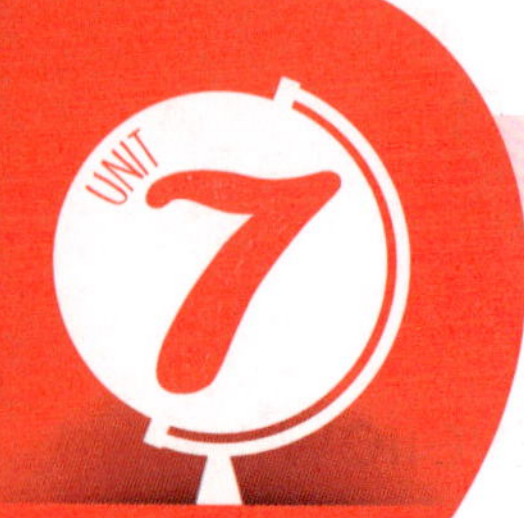

· PRACTICE ·

1 Follow and say.

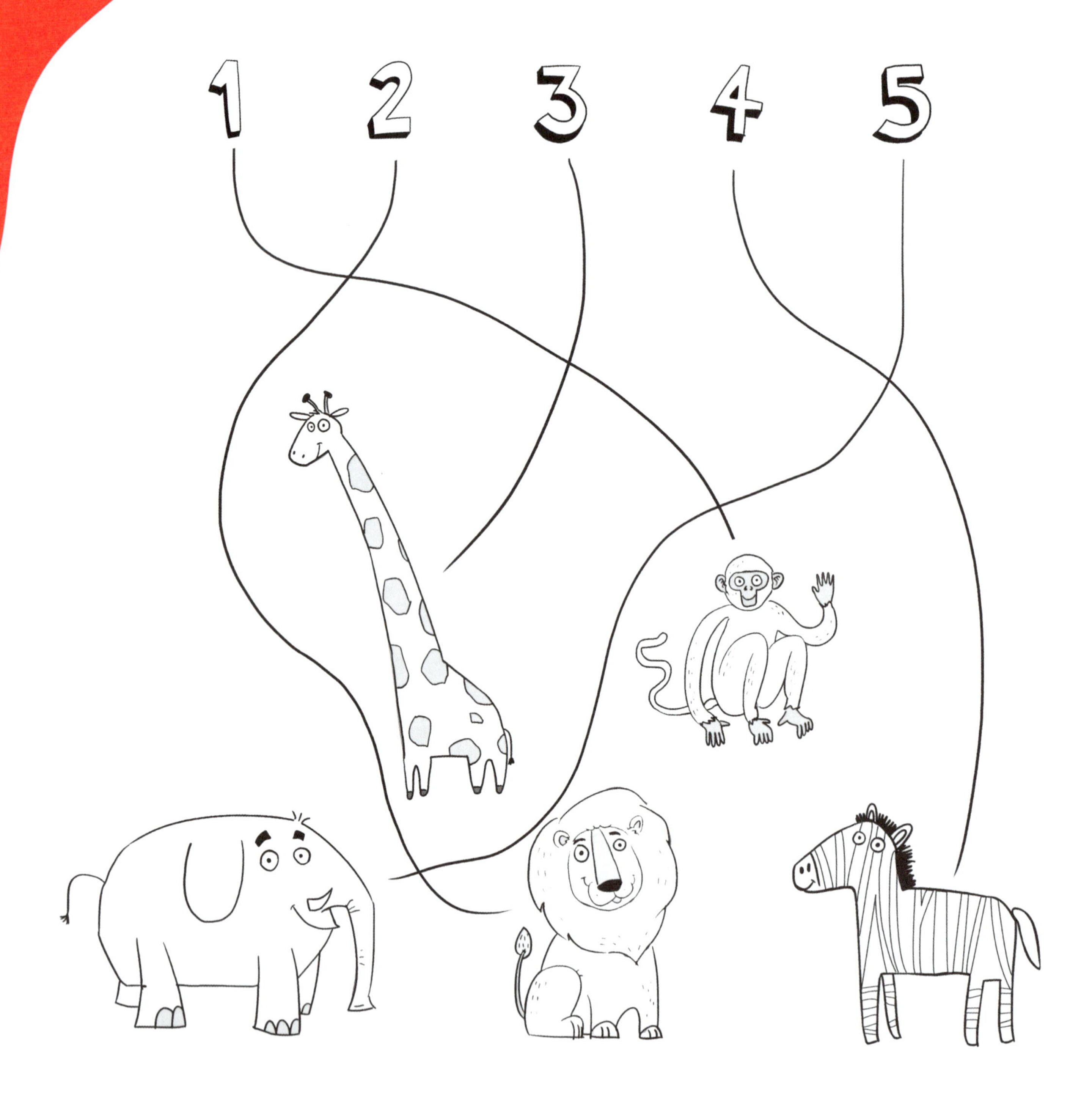

Lesson 4

VOCABULARY

TRACK 76

1 Listen and number.

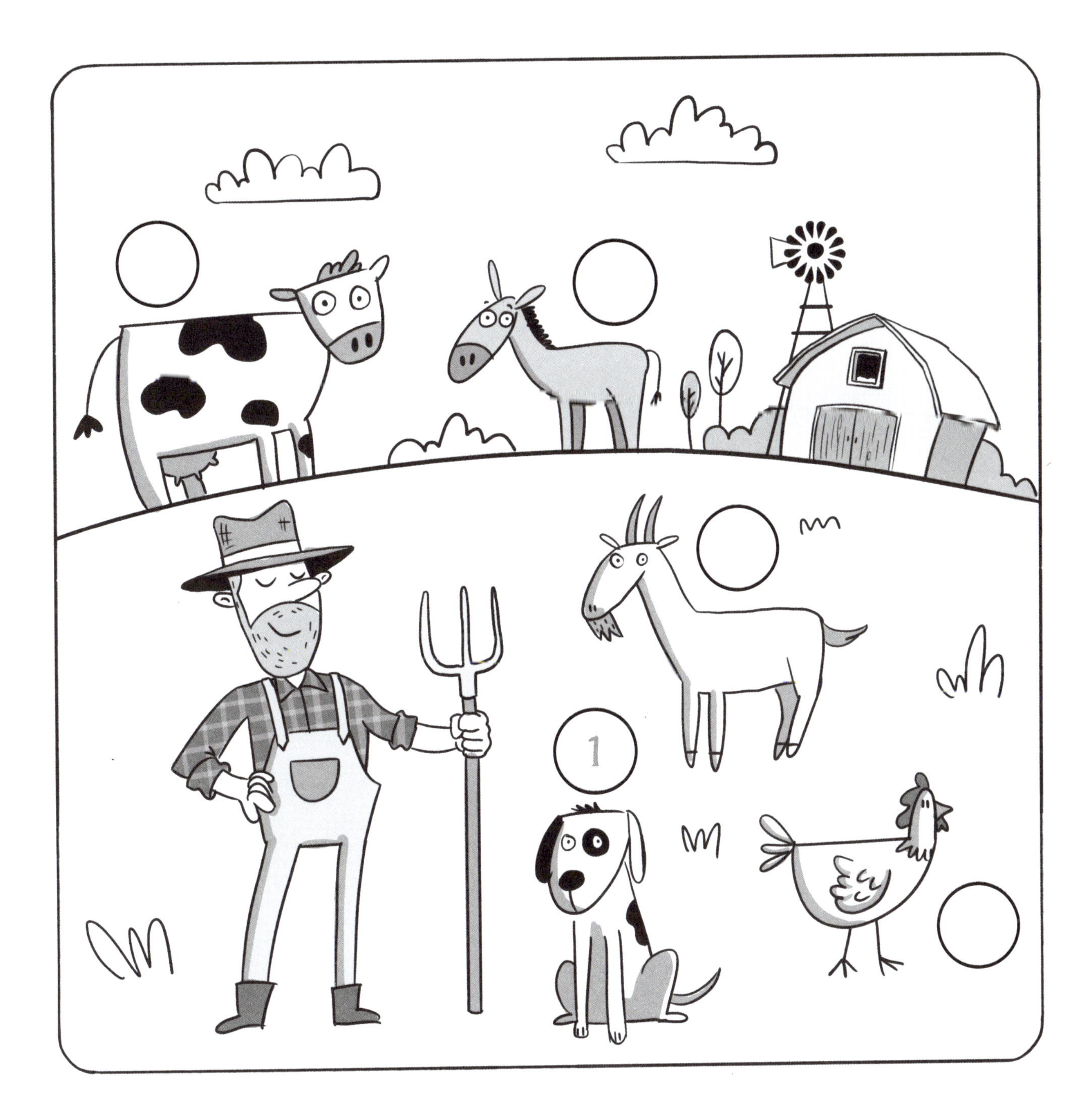

Lesson 5

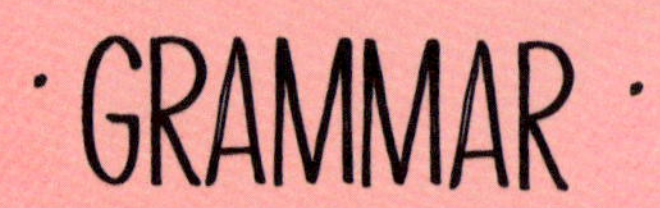

GRAMMAR

They're (hens).

1 Draw and say.

·PRACTICE·

1 Circle and count.

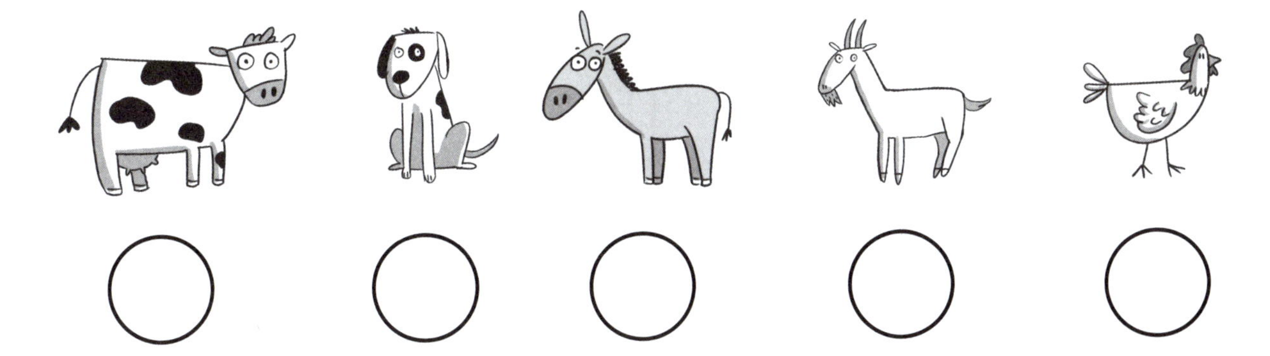

·STORY TIME·

1 Draw.

TRACK 79

1 Listen and circle.

Lesson 1

VOCABULARY

1 Complete.

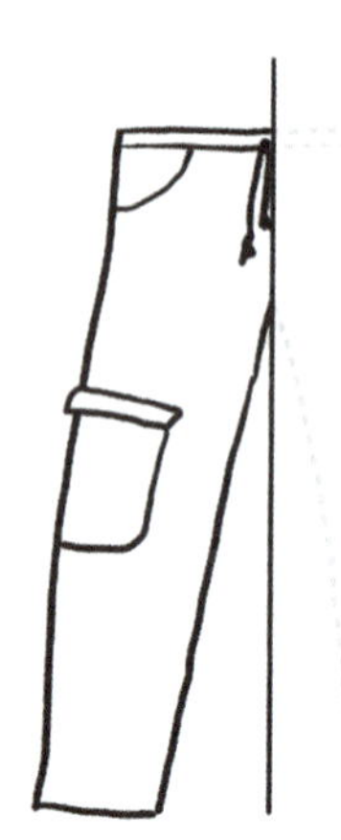

GRAMMAR

It's my (hat).
They're my (pants).

1 Circle.

· PRACTICE ·

1 Draw and say.

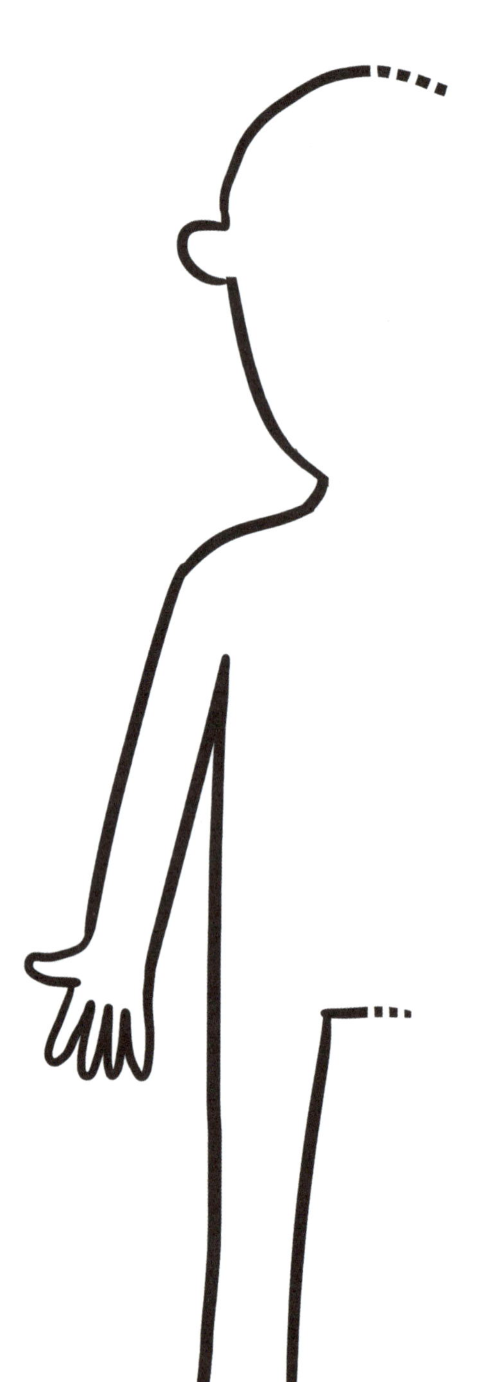

1 Listen and match.

Lesson 5

GRAMMAR

It's your (hat).
They're your (shoes).

1 Draw you and your friend.

1 Match and say.

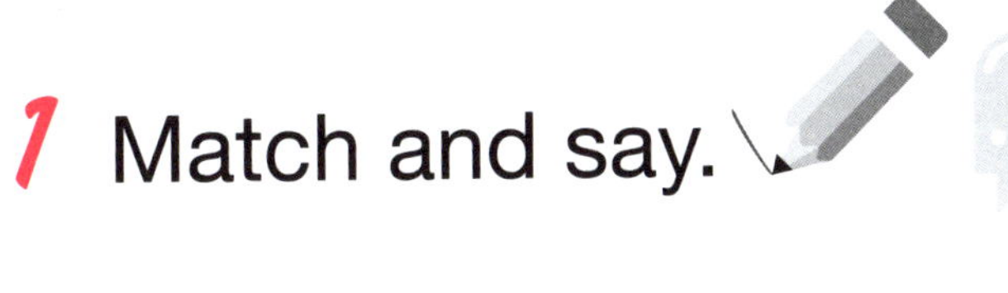

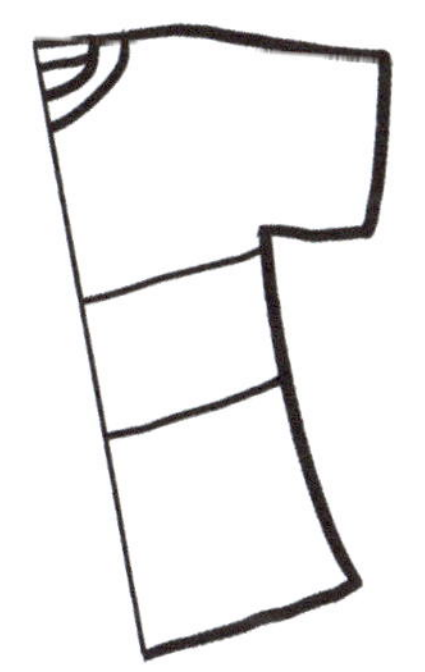

Lesson 7

STORY TIME

1 Number.

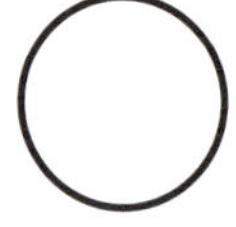

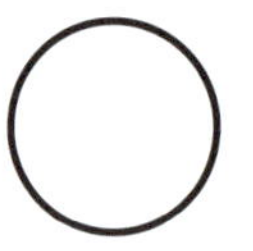

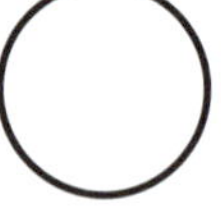

TRACK 89

1 Count and .

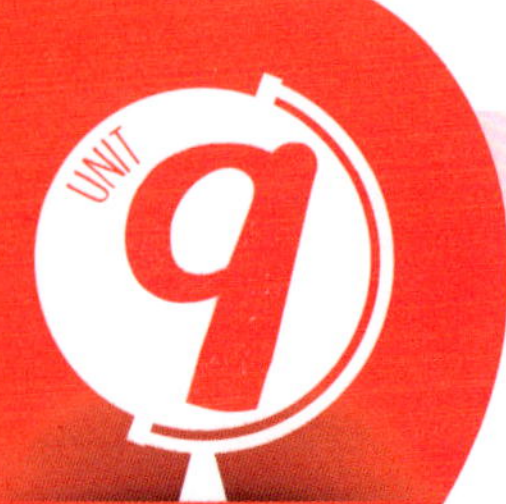
UNIT
9

Lesson 1

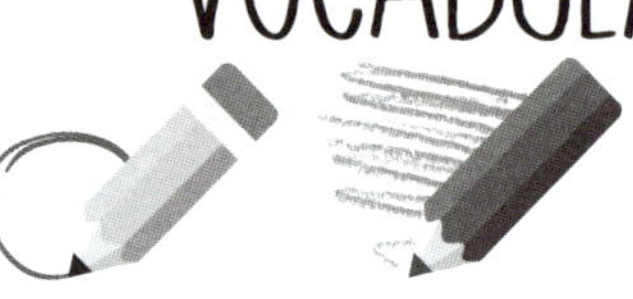
VOCABULARY

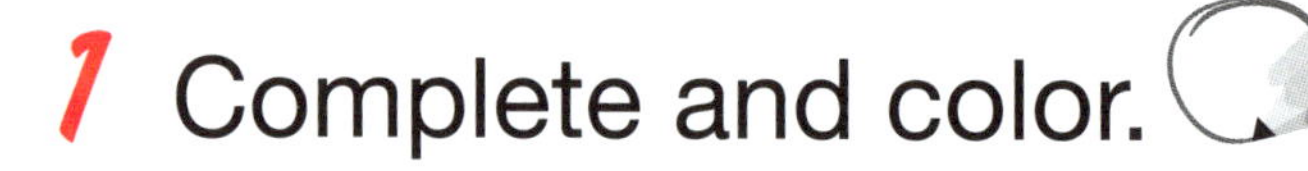
1 Complete and color.

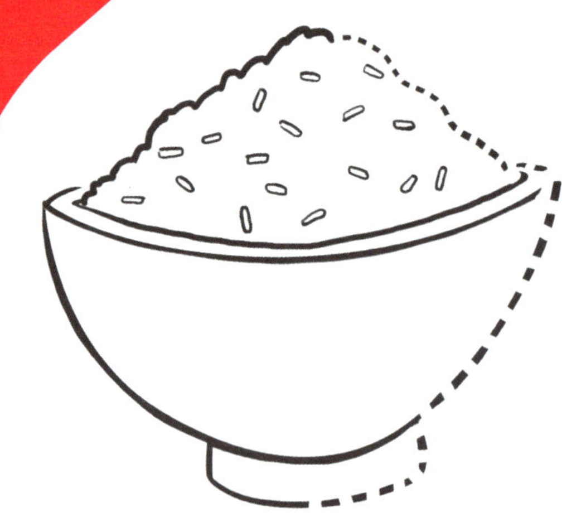

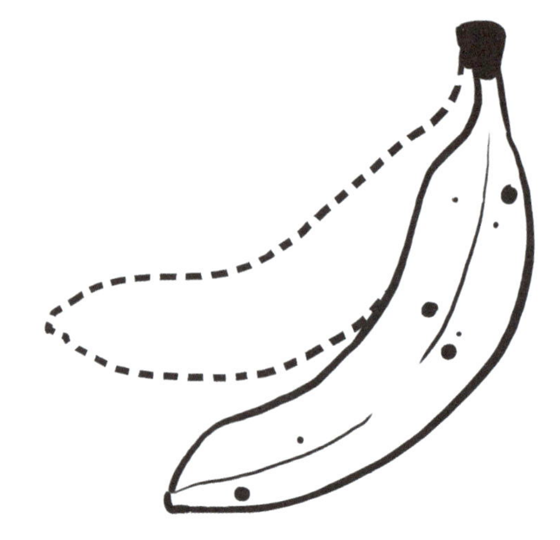

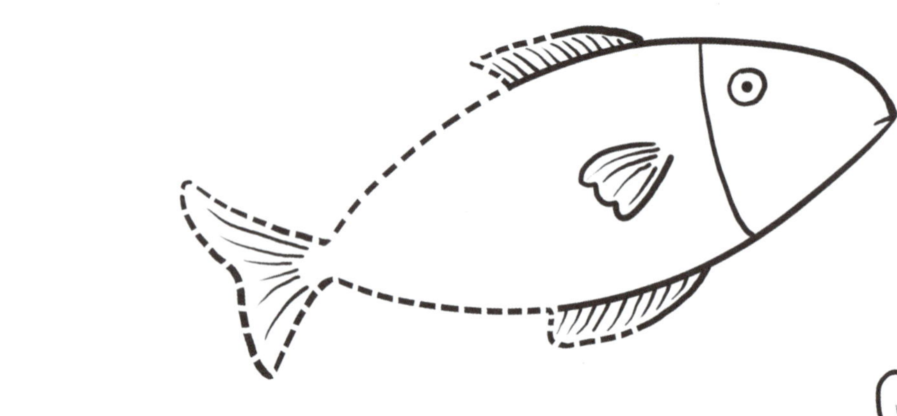

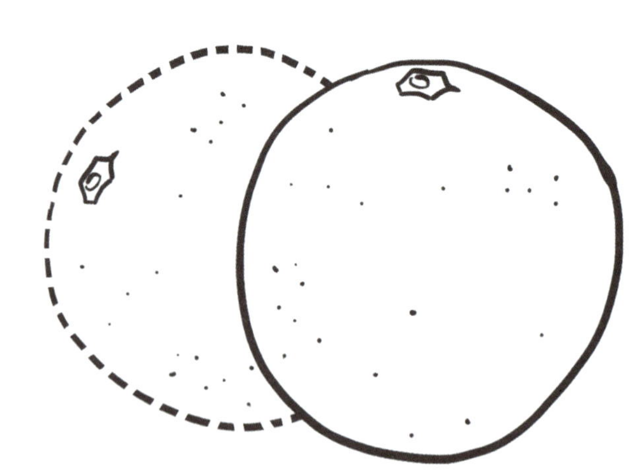

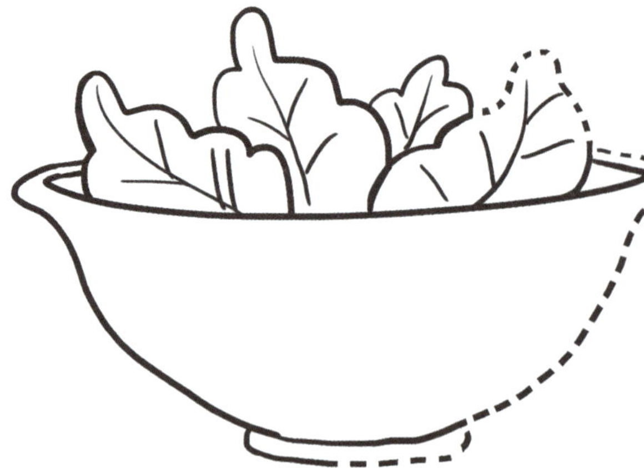

Lesson 2

GRAMMAR

I like (salad).
I don't like (fish).

1 Draw 🙂 or ☹️ and say.

·PRACTICE·

1 Draw and say.

VOCABULARY

TRACK 94

1 Listen and draw.

Lesson 5

GRAMMAR

Do you like (pasta)?
Yes, I do. / No, I don't.

1 Match and draw.

1 Draw ☺ or ☹ for you.

Draw ☺ or ☹ for your friend. 

	you	your friend

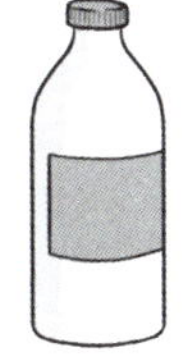		

Lesson 7

STORY TIME

1 Draw.

TRACK 99

1 Listen and draw.

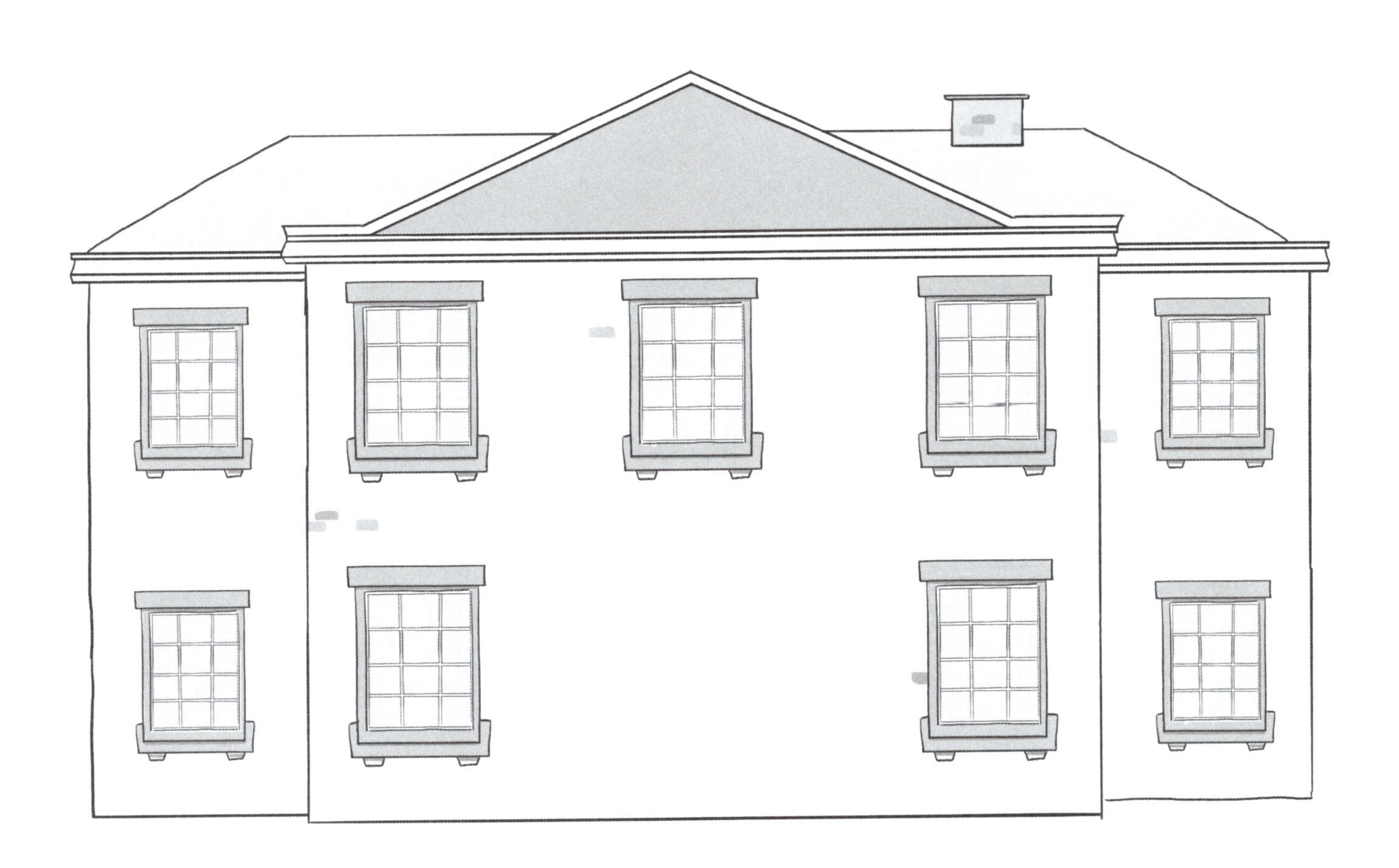

VOCABULARY

1 Number and say.

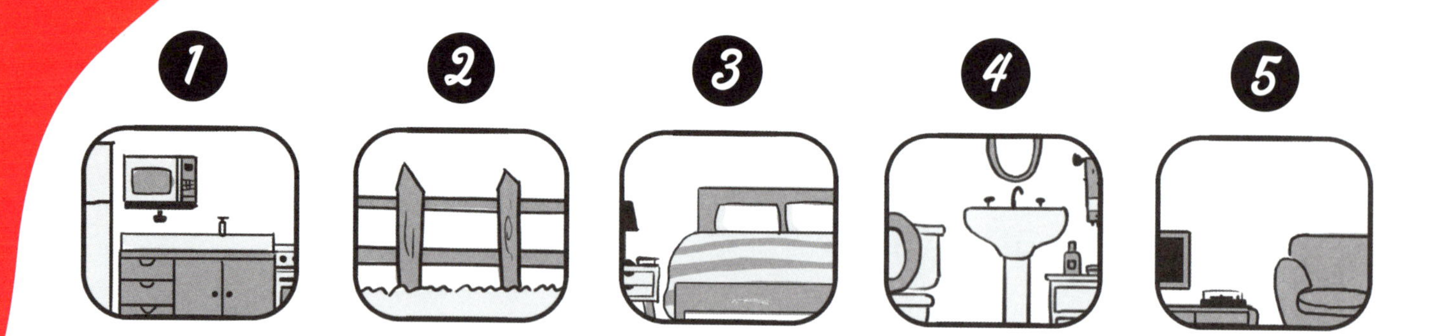

Lesson 2

1 Draw and say.

· GRAMMAR ·

I'm in the (bedroom).

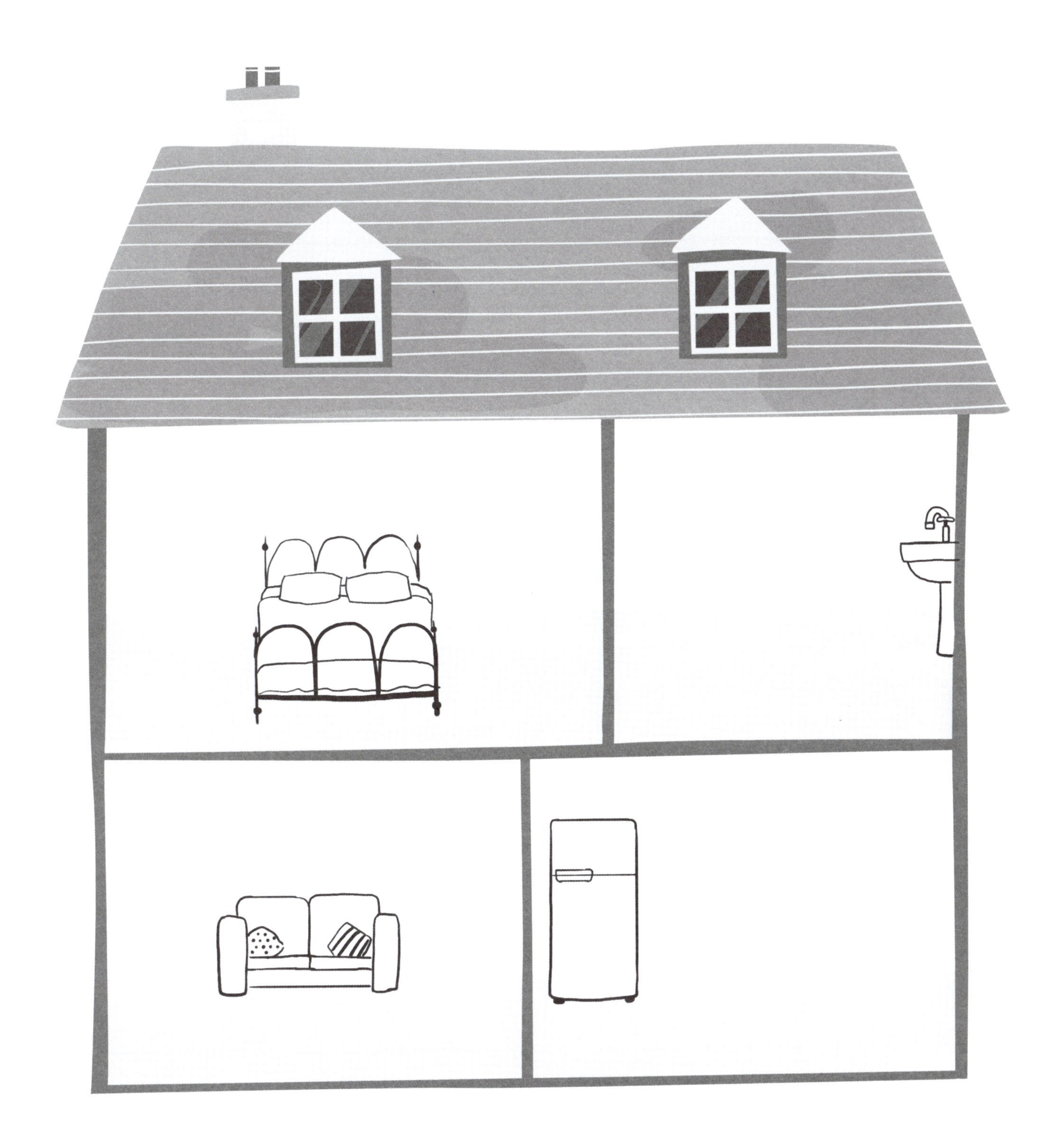

·PRACTICE·

1 Circle and say. 

VOCABULARY

1 Listen and draw.

Lesson 5

GRAMMAR

There's a (bed) in the (bedroom).

1 Write ✗ or ✓.

1 Complete and say.

Lesson 7

· STORY TIME ·

1 Draw.

· TEMPLATE 1 ·

TEMPLATE 2

· TEMPLATE 3 ·

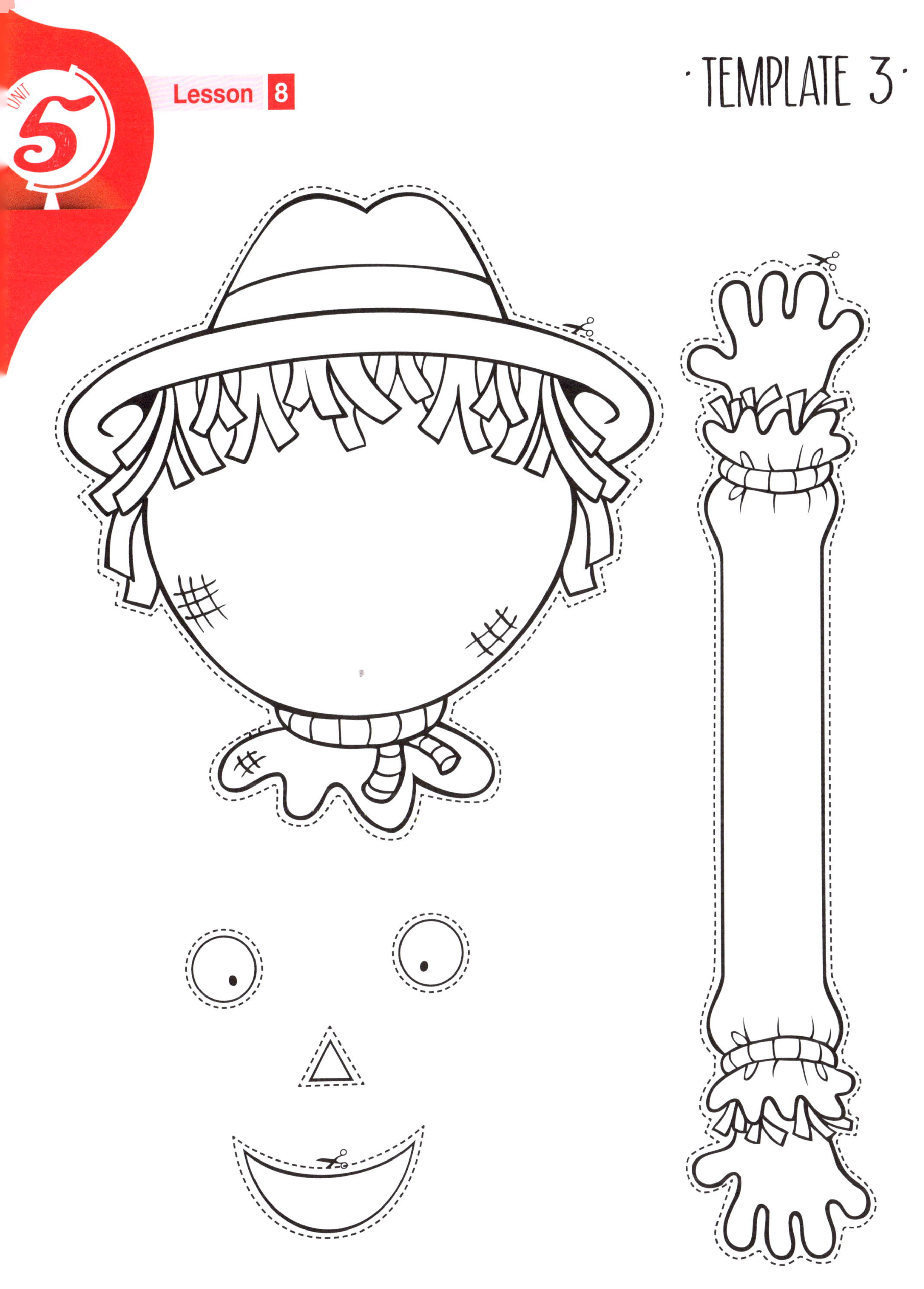

TEMPLATE 4

· TEMPLATE 5 ·

TEMPLATE 6

· TEMPLATE 6 ·

NEXT STATION STARTER PROGRESS RECORD

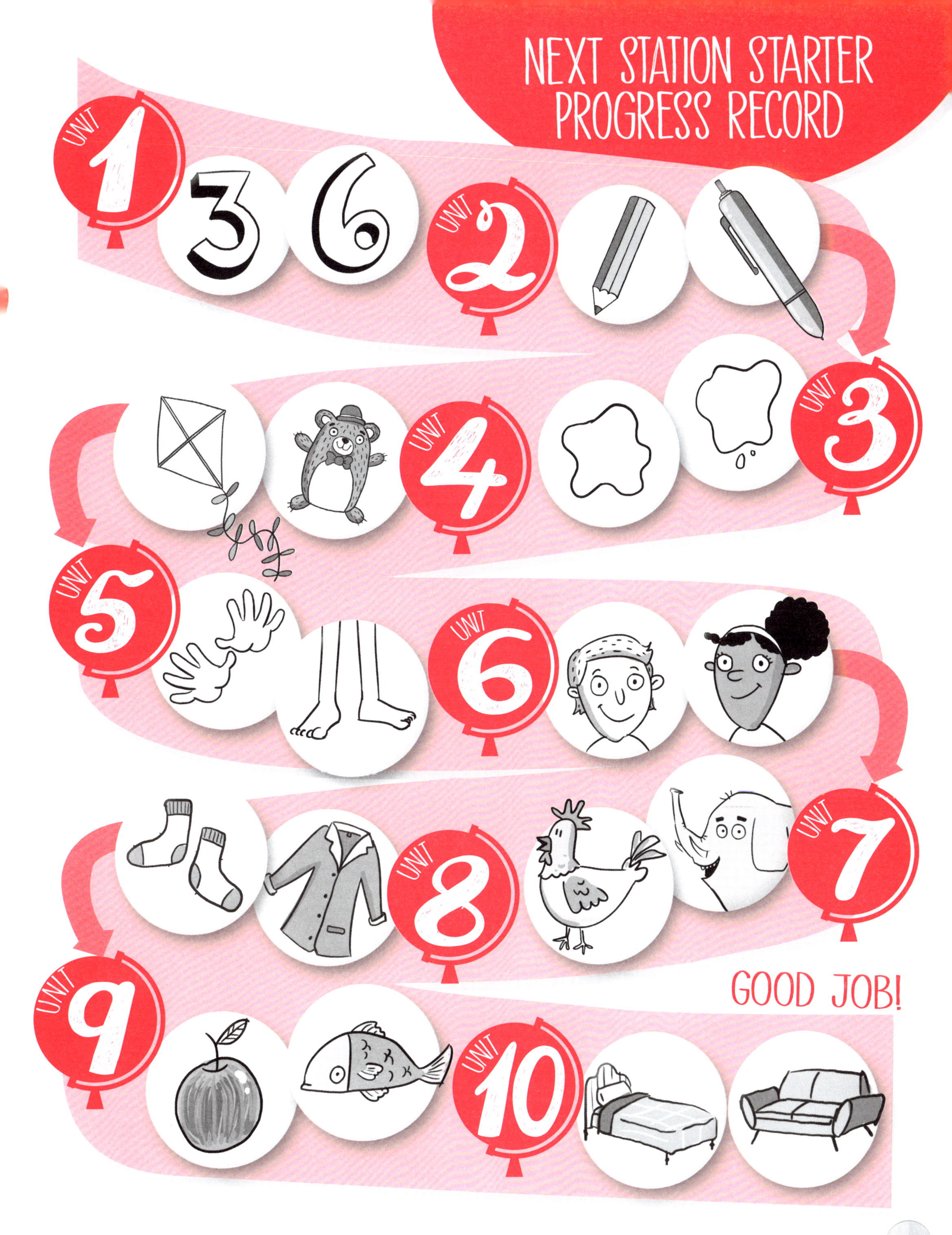

Based on *Next Move*
© Macmillan Publishers Limited 2013
Text © Cantabgilly Limited and Mary Charrington 2013
Next Move is a registered trademark, property of Macmillan Publishers, 2013
First edition entitled "Next Stop" published 2009 by Macmillan Publishers

Director of Languages Brazil: Patrícia Souza De Luccia
Publishing Manager and Field Researcher: Patricia Muradas
Content Creation Coordinator: Cristina do Vale
Art Editor: Jean Aranha
Lead Editors: Ana Beatriz da Costa Moreira, Daniela Gonçala da Costa, Luciana Pereira da Silva
Content Editors: Millyane M. Moura Moreira, Tarsílio Soares Moreira
Digital Editor: Ana Paula Girardi
Editorial Assistant: Roberta Somera
Editorial Intern: Bruna Marques
Art Assistant: Denis Araujo
Art Intern: Jacqueline Alves
Graphic Production: Tatiane Romano, Thais Mendes P. Galvão
Proofreaders: Edward Willson, Márcia Leme, Sabrina Cairo Bileski
Design Concept: Design Divertido Artes Gráficas
Page Make-Up: Figurattiva Editorial
Image Processing: Jean Aranha, Jacqueline Alves, Denis Araujo
Audio: Argila Music, Núcleo de Criação
Cover Concept: Jean Aranha
Cover photography: pmphoto/iStockphoto/Getty Images, Bubert/iStockphoto/Getty Images, LokFung/iStockphoto/Getty Images.
Illustrations: Gustavo Gialuca (p. 3-82, 95) Anthony Rule (p. 83, 85, 87, 89, 91, 93).

We would like to dedicate this book to teachers all over Brazil. We would also like to thank our clients and teachers who have helped us make this book better with their many rich contributions and feedback straight from the classroom!

Dados Internacionais de Catalogação na Publicação (CIP)
Bibliotecária responsável: Aline Graziele Benitez CRB-1/3129

C435n Charrington, Mary
1.ed. Next Station Starter: Workbook / Mary Charrington. – 1.ed. – São Paulo: Macmillan Education do Brasil, 2020.
96 p.; il.; 21 x 27 cm. – (Coleção Next Station)

ISBN: 978-85-511-0136-0

1. Língua inglesa. I. Título. II. Série.
CDD 420

Índice para catálogo sistemático:
1. Língua inglesa

MACMILLAN EDUCATION DO BRASIL
Av. Brigadeiro Faria Lima, 1.309, 3° Andar –
Jd. Paulistano – São Paulo – SP – 01452-002
www.macmillan.com.br
Customer Service: [55] (11) 4613-2278
0800 16 88 77
Fax: [55] (11) 4612-6098

Printed in Brazil. Pancrom 10/2023